ORSON'S FARM™
FEEDS THE FLOCK

℞℞
RAVETTE BOOKS

This edition first published by Ravette Books Limited 1989

Printed and bound in Great Britain
for Ravette Books Limited,
3 Glenside Estate, Star Road, Partridge Green,
Horsham, West Sussex RH13 8RA
by Cox & Wyman Ltd, Reading

ISBN 1 85304 113 0

© 1988 United Feature Syndicate, Inc.

JIM DAVIS 5-18

SLAM

JiM DAViS 5-19

© 1988 United Feature Syndicate, Inc.

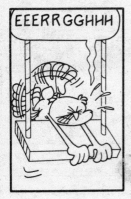

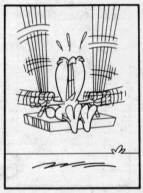

I THINK YOUR TIME WOULD BE BETTER SPENT WITH THESE, BOYS

THANKS, MOM!

JIM DAVIS

6-2

I DON'T THINK THIS IS WHAT ORSON HAD IN MIND

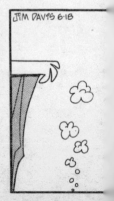

© 1988 United Feature Syndicate, Inc.

© 1988 United Feature Syndicate, Inc.

JiM DAViS 6-27

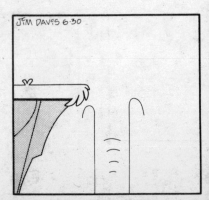

© 1988 United Feature Syndicate, Inc.

JRM DAVIS   7-5

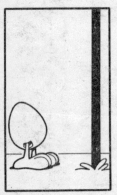

JIM DAVIS

7-8

BLAT

JIM DAVIS 7-13

© 1988 United Feature Syndicate, Inc.

© 1988 United Feature Syndicate, Inc.

JiM DAViS 7-27

WHAT IN THE WORLD IS THAT?

WADE GOT A NEW BULB FOR HIS NIGHT LIGHT

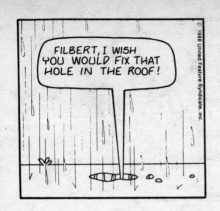

JIM DAVIS   8-13

BOY, I HATE IT WHEN THAT HAPPENS

© 1988 United Feature Syndicate, Inc.

© 1988 United Feature Syndicate, Inc.

8-29

JiM DAViS

© 1988 United Feature Syndicate, Inc.

8-30

JIM DAVIS

CHOO

JiM DAViS

9-13

© 1988 United Feature Syndicate, Inc.

JIM DAVIS   9-16

CHOCK

JIM DAVIS   9-20

© 1988 United Feature Syndicate, Inc.

I LOVE DOING THAT

JIM DAVIS

9-24

Other JIM DAVIS books published by Ravette

In this series
Goes Half Hog! 1	**£1.95**
Goes Half Hog! 2	**£1.95**
Counts Its Chickens 1	**£1.95**
Counts Its Chickens 2	**£1.95**
Rules The Roost 1	**£1.95**
Rules The Roost 2	**£1.95**
Sows The Seed	**£1.95**

Garfield Pocket books
No. 1	**Garfield The Great Lover**	**£1.95**
No. 2	**Garfield Why Do You Hate Mondays?**	**£1.95**
No. 3	**Garfield Does Pooky Need You?**	**£1.95**
No. 4	**Garfield Admit It, Odie's OK!**	**£1.95**
No. 5	**Garfield Two's Company**	**£1.95**
No. 6	**Garfield What's Cooking?**	**£1.95**
No. 7	**Garfield Who's Talking?**	**£1.95**
No. 8	**Garfield Strikes Again**	**£1.95**
No. 9	**Garfield Here's Looking At You**	**£1.95**
No. 10	**Garfield We Love You Too**	**£1.95**
No. 11	**Garfield Here We Go Again**	**£1.95**
No. 12	**Garfield Life and Lasagne**	**£1.95**
No. 13	**Garfield In The Pink**	**£1.95**
No. 14	**Garfield Just Good Friends**	**£1.95**
No. 15	**Garfield Plays It Again**	**£1.95**
No. 16	**Garfield Flying High**	**£1.95**
No. 17	**Garfield On Top Of The World**	**£1.95**
No. 18	**Garfield Happy Landings**	**£1.95**

All these books are available at your local bookshop or news-agent, or can be ordered direct from the publisher. Just tick the titles you require and fill in the form below. Prices and availability subject to change without notice. A full list of our publications is available. Please send your request to the address below.

Ravette Books Limited, 3 Glenside Estate, Star Road, Partridge Green, Horsham, West Sussex RH13 8RA

Please send a cheque or postal order, and allow the following for postage and packing. UK: 45p for up to two books and 15p for each additional book.

Name ....

Address ....

....